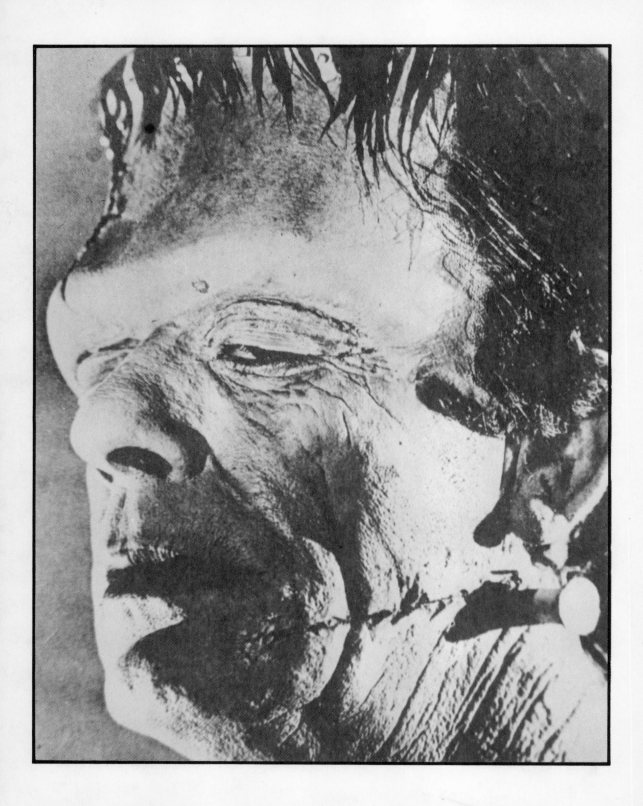

FRANKENSTEIN

by Ian Thorne

Reprinted 1978

Library of Congress Catalog Card Number: 76-051144.

International Standard Book Numbers:
0-913940-66-6 Library Bound
0-913940-73-9 Paperback

Design - Doris Woods and Randal M. Heise.

FRANKENSTEIN

FRANKENSTEIN'S MONSTER

It was a movie like no other.

Before it started, there was a warning. This was to be the story of Frankenstein, a scientist who tried to play God by making a man. The story would be shocking. It would be horrifying. Timid people in the audience were invited to leave!

And then the story began in a graveyard . . .

Henry Frankenstein and Fritz, his helper, hid behind a tombstone. They made sure nobody was watching. Then they came out and dug up a coffin. The coffin and the body inside were carried away on a cart. Frankenstein said:

"He isn't dead. He's just waiting for a new life."

Frankenstein planned to bring the dead body back to life by means of scientific skill. But first, he needed a human brain.

He sent Fritz to a nearby medical school to steal one!

Fritz found two jars, each with a brain. One was labeled NORMAL BRAIN. Fritz grabbed it — and dropped it! The brain was ruined.

So Fritz had to take the other jar. The brain inside was that of a criminal, a murderer. No matter. Frankenstein had sent Fritz to get a brain and Fritz always obeyed.

Fritz brought the brain to his master's lab. It was in Castle Frankenstein, on a mountain in Germany. The young scientist put the brain into the body he had prepared. He and Fritz got the life-giving machine ready. It was a stormy night and the machine needed lightning to make it work.

Suddenly, there was a pounding at the castle door. Three people demanded to be let in.

One of them was Frankenstein's teacher from medical school, Professor Waldman. The second was Frankenstein's friend, Victor Moritz. And the third was Frankenstein's lovely bride-to-be, Elizabeth. They had learned of Frankenstein's strange experiments. They were afraid he was going mad.

Frankenstein said to them: "You will see whether I'm crazy or not!"

The friends of Henry Frankenstein plead with him to stop his experiments. From left to right: Professor Waldman (Edward van Sloan), Victor Moritz (John Boles), Fritz (Dwight Frye), Elizabeth (Mae Clarke), Frankenstein (Colin Clive).

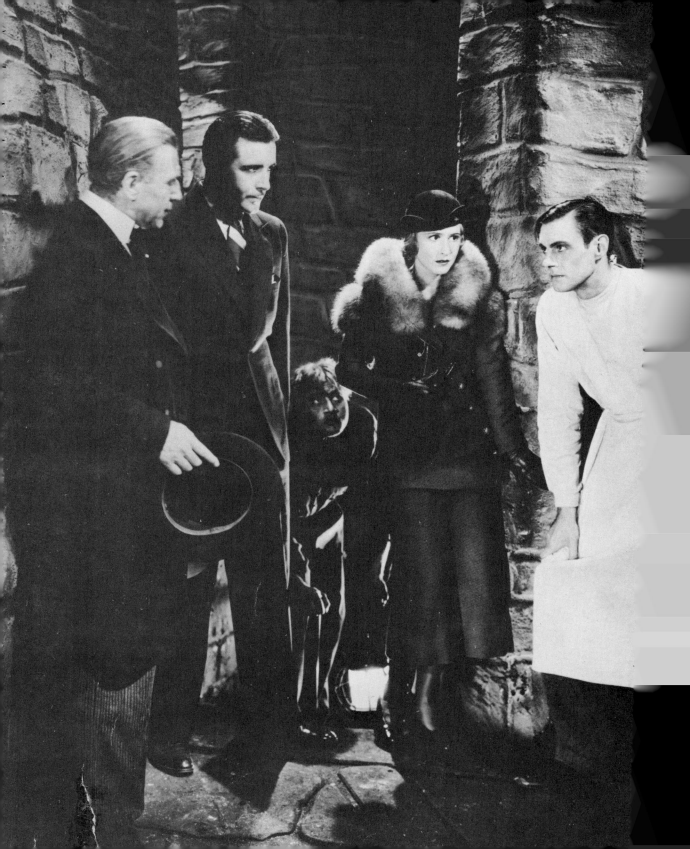

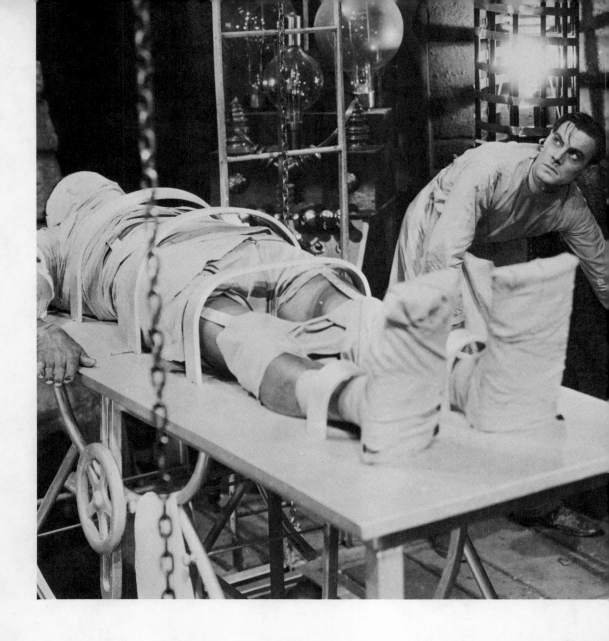

The three visitors watched Frankenstein carry out
his experiment. The body, on a table, was lifted high
into a tower. There lightning struck it with a blinding
flash. The life-giving machine did its work.

The body was lowered again to the lab. And
Frankenstein came closer to look at it. Had the experiment worked?

Frankenstein and Fritz turn on the machine to animate the creature.

A finger — a hand — an arm moved.
"It's alive!" screamed Frankenstein. "Alive!"
Elizabeth, Victor and the Professor tried to calm him. Frankenstein said: "Now I know what it feels like to be God!"

In the days that followed, Frankenstein left the castle. He and Fritz took their newly made "man" to an old windmill where nobody would bother them.

Professor Waldman came to Frankenstein and begged him to lock up the creature. "He has a criminal brain," Waldman said. "He will prove dangerous."

Frankenstein only laughed. Waldman repeated his warning. "Evil will come of this. You have created a monster, and it will destroy you. Think of Elizabeth!"

"Elizabeth believes in me," said Frankenstein. "I must do further experiments."

As the two men argued, the sound of footsteps echoed in the old mill. The creature was coming. He entered the room. He was tall, and large with deep-sunk eyes. He, however, did obey Frankenstein's simple commands.

"He is like a child," the scientist said.

The monster changed. Fritz came running into the room, carrying a torch. The bright flames drove the creature crazy. He tried to escape. He refused to obey Frankenstein.

"He is as strong as ten men!" Frankenstein shouted. Finally, he and Fritz bound the creature with ropes and put him in the cellar.

The child-like brain of the creature dwelt within a powerful body.

Frankenstein and Waldman went away, but Fritz stayed. He hated the creature. He began to torment the monster with the torch. The monster came for him . . .

Upstairs in the mill, Frankenstein and Waldman heard a terrible scream. "It's Fritz!" cried the young scientist. He and Waldman dashed back to the cellar. But it was too late. The monster had killed for the first time.

Waldman and Frankenstein subdued the monster with a hypo. "It must be put to death," said the Professor.

Frankenstein saw his life-work spoiled. The shock was too much for him. He broke down. Elizabeth and Frankenstein's father took the young man away to help him recover.

Meanwhile, Waldman could not resist examining the monster before destroying him. As the old man bent over the creature — the creature awoke!

With one hard blow, the monster broke Waldman's neck. Then the creature ran away into the dark countryside.

Frankenstein and Waldman attempt to subdue the creature.

For many days, nothing was heard of the monster. Henry Frankenstein, nursed by Elizabeth, recovered his health. His experiments seemed like a bad dream that had passed. The young couple planned their wedding. The whole village was invited to share the happiness of the House of Frankenstein.

A poor woodsman lived in a hut by a nearby lake. He had a little daughter named Maria. "Play for awhile," Maria's father said. "Then we will go to the village and have a grand time at the wedding."

Maria went down to the lake shore to pick daisies. Suddenly, a huge figure loomed over her. "Who are you?" asked Maria. The person did not answer. "Play with me," said Maria.

It was the monster, come out of hiding. His mind was like that of a child. He smiled as Maria gave him flowers. Then he and the little girl had fun tossing the pretty daisies into the water.

They floated! That was fun. Pretty things were floating on the water.

But then all the daisies were gone. There were no more pretty things to toss in. But wait! The monster had a fine idea. He would toss in pretty Maria and she would float, too.

He came toward her, smiling . . .

Back at Castle Frankenstein, Henry and Elizabeth got ready for their wedding. Elizabeth was very moody.

"I am afraid," she said. "Why isn't Dr. Waldman at the wedding?"

Frankenstein said, "You are just nervous."

"Something is coming between us," she insisted.

At that moment, Victor burst in. "It's Dr. Waldman!" he said.

Frankenstein knew what had happened. He locked Elizabeth in her room for safety. Then he and the other men began to search the castle.

The thing they were afraid of had happened. The monster had returned to the place where he was "born."

As Elizabeth sat in her room, the monster came in through a window. She was very pretty, thought the monster. She was like Maria . . .

In another part of the castle, Frankenstein and Victor heard Elizabeth scream. They rushed to her room. They found her lying where the monster had dropped her before escaping.

But she was alive.

"Don't let it come here," she said.

Down in the village, people were dancing and
singing. Suddenly they fell silent. The woodsman came
walking down the street. He was carrying Maria.

He brought her to the village leader, the
Burgomaster. "She's been murdered! Drowned!"

"Justice will be done," said the Burgomaster.

When Frankenstein heard the news, he went to
the village. "I made the monster with my hands," he
said. "With these hands I will destroy him."

He turned to Victor. "I leave Elizabeth in your care.
Whatever happens."

20

A mob of villagers vow to destroy Maria's killer.

The villagers set out to search for the monster. Waving torches, they took police dogs and broke into groups. Frankenstein led a mob into the mountains.

Mist covered the cliffs. One searcher took his dogs into the rocks and the monster struck.

Frankenstein found the man lying broken on the ground. "Over there . . ." the man said.

"Come on!" said Frankenstein. "This way!"

Frankenstein rushed on ahead. Bearing his torch, he climbed over the rocks. He knew that his creature was there somewhere . . .

Suddenly, the monster rose up from behind a rock.

Frankenstein and his creation stared silently at each other. Then the monster advanced — staring, always staring at the man who had given him life.

Frankenstein realized, almost too late, that he was in great danger. He thrust the blazing torch at the monster. But the creature was no longer afraid of fire.

He came closer. He reached out. His arms closed about the struggling scientist.

Frankenstein shouted for help. The villagers heard his cries and came running.

"Turn the dogs loose!" said the Burgomaster.

Frankenstein lay on the ground, stunned by a blow from the monster. As the yelping dogs came closer, the monster picked up the body of his creator. He began to run to the old mill where Frankenstein had once hidden him away.

The villagers ran to the mill and began to batter its door. The monster peered down at them and they yelled with rage.

Frankenstein awoke and realized he was the monster's prisoner. He was not afraid, however. He had only one thought — to kill the evil thing he had made. He and the monster struggled on the balcony of the windmill. The horrified men of the village watched as the monster threw Frankenstein off the mill.

"He's alive!" somebody shouted, bending over the unconscious scientist.

"Take him to the village," ordered the Burgomaster.

Far above, the monster grinned down at the mob. No one was willing to go in and get him. Then one man had an idea.

"Burn the mill! Burn it down!"

Torches were thrown into the dead grass near the windmill's base. Strong winds caught the flames and blew them high.

The mob of villagers stood watching. The monster fled from the balcony as the flames spread. The walls of the mill were all on fire. The windmill arms burst into flame. Before long, the whole windmill was burning.

The monster, trapped inside, tried to side step falling timbers. Once more he was afraid of fire. It faced him at every turn. Get away! Get away! But he could not.

A large beam from the roof caved in. It pinned the monster to the floor and he began to scream.

Outside, the men stood quietly and watched the mill burn to the ground. Then they went home to the village.

At the castle, Elizabeth and the young scientist's father gave Frankenstein gentle care. He was put to bed. His friends knew that Henry Frankenstein would recover. The nightmare of Frankenstein's monster was over . . .

And so the great movie ended.

The monster had died in the flames. But had he, really? Movie audiences loved the thrills of Frankenstein. And so the monster never died.

He is alive and well today!

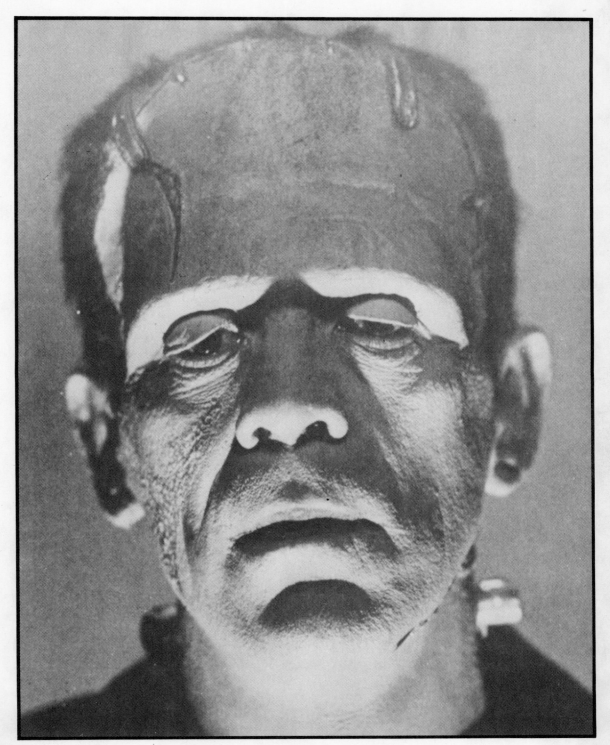

Mary Wollstonecraft Shelley, author of Frankenstein.

Frankenstein was created by a woman.

The original story, Frankenstein, or The Modern Prometheus, was written by Mary Wollstonecraft Godwin in 1816 and published two years later. When Mary began the story, she was only 18 years old.

It was a rainy, gloomy summer, that of 1816. Mary was staying at a Swiss villa on Lake Geneva. Her friends were the poets Percy Bysshe Shelley (whom she later married) and Lord Byron, Mary's step-sister Claire Clairmont, and Byron's friend, Dr. John Polidari.

The friends were supposed to have been reading ghost stories one stormy night. Byron suggested that each of them write a ghost story. Mary's original tale, written over a period of months, was Frankenstein.

Percy Shelley helped his wife improve the final manuscript. At first, the author had trouble finding a publisher. Three turned it down. But when it finally appeared in print, it became a best seller. No one knew Mary had written it. Her name did not appear on the first edition. Most readers thought the author was Shelley.

In 1831 it became known that Mary was the author. The book was published in many languages. Plays were written based upon it. Mary Shelley wrote other books. But Frankenstein is the only one that gained lasting fame.

The only surviving picture from Edison's **Frankenstein** *shows a shaggy monster.*

The first movie based on Frankenstein was a silent film made in 1910. It was produced by the great Thomas Alva Edison and featured Charles Ogle as the monster.

Unfortunately, all prints of this old movie seem to have disappeared. Reviewers of the time praised it. They said the creation of the monster in a vat of blazing chemicals was unforgettable.

Edison's Frankenstein ends with the young scientist sorry about his desire to "play God." Frankenstein turns to Elizabeth, his true love. And the monster disappears into thin air!

A second version, "Life Without Soul," was made in New York in 1915. But it was not until 1931 that Frankenstein gained lasting fame as a movie.

Universal Pictures had scored a great success with Dracula, starring Bela Lugosi. They wanted to do another horror film right away — and chose Frankenstein. Lugosi was to have played the monster. But he refused to do a role without speaking.

The studio turned to an unknown English-born actor named William Henry Pratt. His stage name was Boris Karloff. He played the monster perfectly. Without saying a word, he made the creature both horrifying and sad.

Boris Karloff (1887-1969) became the king of horror films. He played not only Frankenstein's monster, but also the Mummy, Dr. Fu Manchu, and assorted mad scientists. Late in his career, he hosted a TV horror show.

The Bride of Frankenstein was played by Elsa Lanchester. Dr. Praetorius was portrayed by the wonderful Ernest Thesiger.

Universal's Frankenstein starred Colin Clive as the scientist. Still, the real star was Boris Karloff. The movie was a box-office smash.

In 1935, Karloff starred in Bride of Frankenstein. Taking a hint from Mary Shelley's original story, Frankenstein and the mad Dr. Praetorius set out to create a mate for the monster. (In this movie he had not burned up in the mill after all. He fell into an underground cistern and survived.)

The Bride, played by Elsa Lanchester, is put together and given life. She looks at her intended mate and screams with terror.

Poor monster! Mad with sorrow, he blows up the

laboratory. Once again, he seems to have been destroyed.

After this second movie, nearly everyone referred to the monster himself as "Frankenstein." The name became part of the language. A Frankenstein was a thing that turned on its creator and destroyed him.

Son of Frankenstein continued the story of the monster in 1939. Like the first two films, it was well-made and very scary. Karloff starred, together with Basil Rathbone as the son of the late Henry Frankenstein.

Baron Wolf von Frankenstein comes to the village of his ancestors. It is 25 years since the monster disappeared.

A mad shepherd named Ygor (played by Lugosi) tells Frankenstein the monster is not dead. Ygor leads the Baron to the depths of the castle. There lies the monster, in a coma.

"Cannot die," says Ygor. "Your father make him live for always!"

The Baron cannot resist giving back full life to the monster. It walks again, it kills again, and it dies again, kicked into a pit of boiling sulfur by the sturdy Baron.

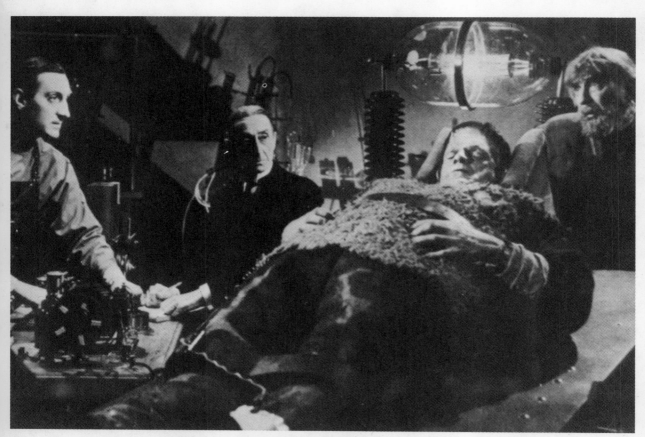

The son of Frankenstein (Basil Rathbone, left) re-animates the monster as his butler (Edgar Norton) assists. At right is Bela Lugosi, playing Ygor.

Lon Chaney, Jr. as the monster in Ghost of Frankenstein.

Karloff was now tired of the monster role, which had made him a star. Also, he felt that scriptwriters were losing sight of the basic "childlike" nature of the creature. He was becoming evil rather than misunderstood.

Ghost of Frankenstein, released in 1942, saw Lon Chaney, Jr. playing the monster. The monster, pried out of a block of solid sulfur, is given a new brain. The brain is that of Ygor! The monster becomes a raging maniac and seems to die in the movie's flaming ending.

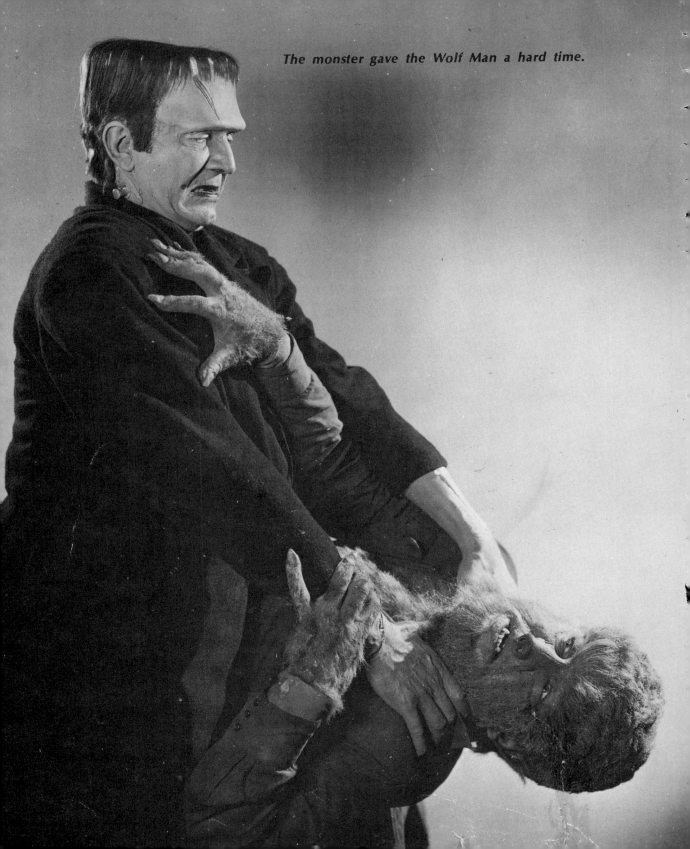

The monster gave the Wolf Man a hard time.

In 1943, movie-goers were given two monsters for the price of one in Frankenstein Meets the Wolf Man. Bela Lugosi played the monster while Lon Chaney, Jr. played the Wolf Man. This time, the creature seemed to drown when villagers blew up the dam.

The immortal monster was back the following year in House of Frankenstein. This time, he was played by cowboy actor Glenn Strange. The movie also featured Dracula, the Wolf Man, and a mad scientist played by Karloff himself.

Glenn Strange played the creature in House of Frankenstein. A closeup of Strange appears on page 2. The actor later played a friendly bartender on the Gunsmoke TV series.

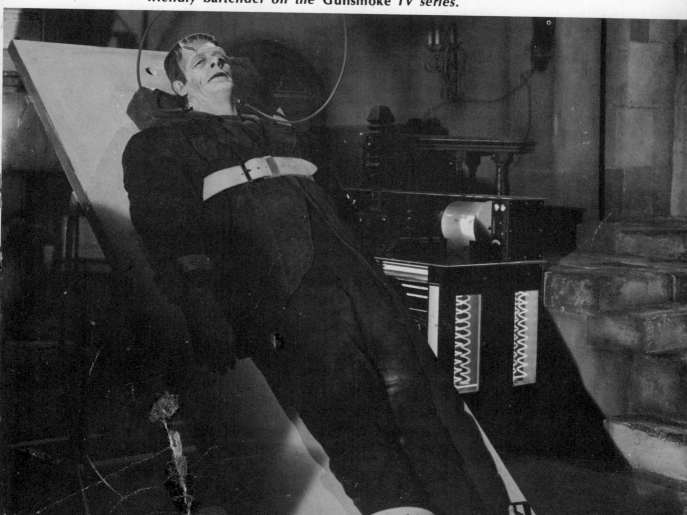

House of Dracula (1945) featured the monster in a fairly minor role. Once again, Glenn Strange was the creature.

The last of the Universal movies about Frankenstein was the most unusual. Abbott and Costello Meet Frankenstein (1948) blended humor and horror. It was a classic film comedy.

Another comedy about the monster, Young Frankenstein, was made by Mel Brooks in 1974. It was a funny film too, and was the story of the Frankenstein's son.

Glenn Strange menaces Lou Costello (left) and Bud Abbott.

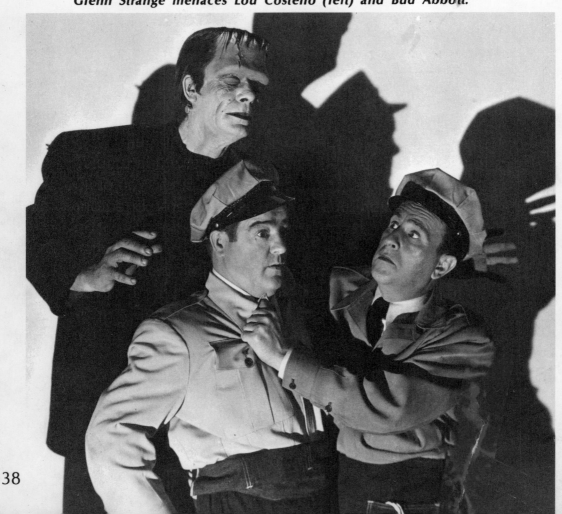

Herman Munster was played by Fred Gwynne.

The original Frankenstein monster disappeared from movie theaters after 1948. But he was not forgotten. Television brought back the old movies. A whole new generation of children saw Frankenstein and shivered. But the children also loved the monster. They wrote letters to Karloff, who said:

"Children seemed to understand that he was the victim of something beyond his control. He was bewildered and afraid."

A comedy TV series called "The Munsters" came out in 1964 and was a great hit. Herman Munster, the lovable father of the series, looked almost exactly like Frankenstein's monster.

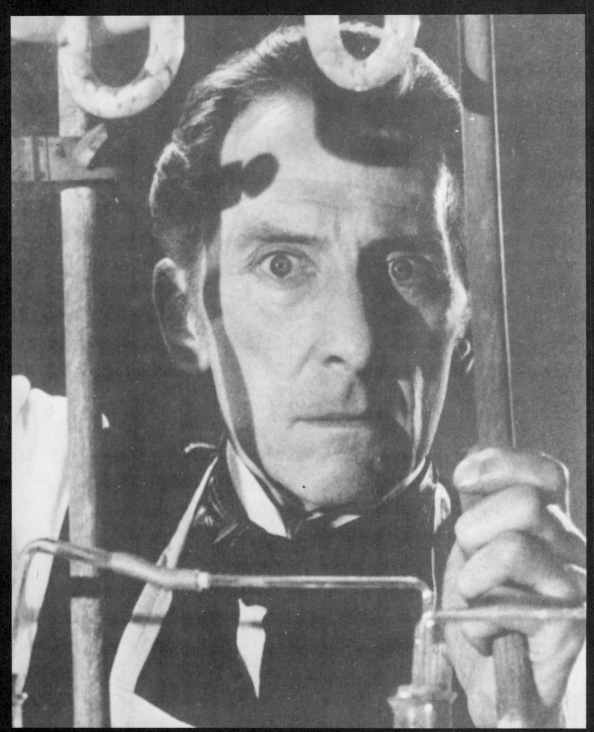

Peter Cushing as Dr. Frankenstein.

Frankenstein returned to movie screens in 1957. Two films, one good and one awful, appeared that year. The bad one was, "I was a Teenage Frankenstein," made in Hollywood. The good one was, "Curse of Frankenstein," made in England by Hammer Films.

Hammer's Frankenstein was the first full-color version of the story. The scientist was played by Peter Cushing. The monster was portrayed by Christopher Lee. Curse of Frankenstein was vivid, chilling, and very gory. It was a huge success. Hammer made many other films with a Frankenstein theme. But none were up to the standard of their first effort.

Christopher Lee's monster proved that they just don't make them now the way they used to.

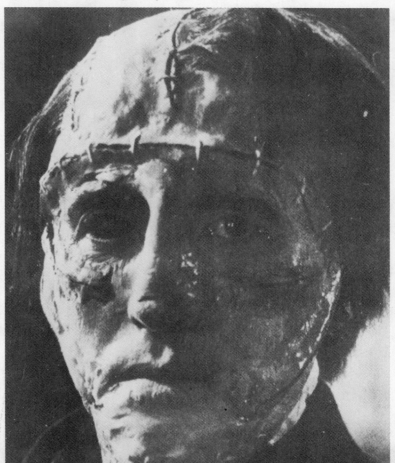

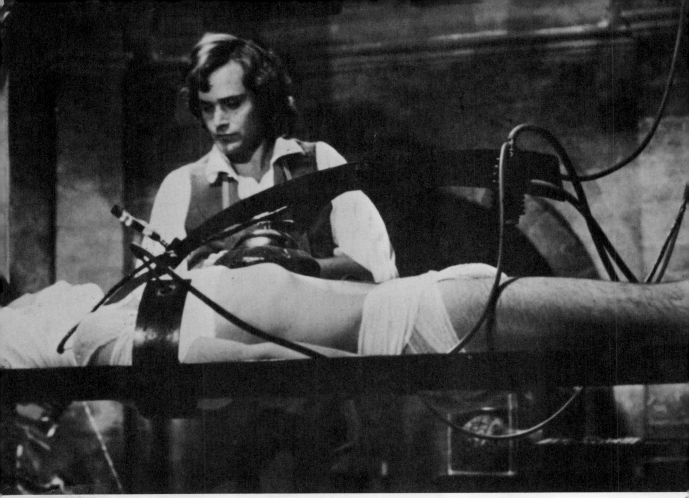

Leonard Whiting, as Frankenstein, prepares to give life to the creature in the 1974 TV version of the true story.

If you read Mary Shelley's Frankenstein, you are in for a surprise. Her story is quite a bit different from that of most of the movies about the man-made monster. The only film that even came close to telling Mary's story was a television special made in 1974, Frankenstein: The True Story.

Mary's book begins with the strange tale of a sea captain. Sailing in Arctic seas amid the ice, the captain sees a strange figure. It is a very tall man driving a dog sled over the packed ice.

Shortly afterward, the captain sees a second sled and driver. This man is nearly dead from exposure. The captain takes him on board. All this man can think about is following the first sled.

The rescued man is a scientist, Victor Frankenstein. The figure he was following is the monster.

Frankenstein tells his awful story. He was a student of chemistry and anatomy. He dreamed of creating a living man and put together a huge body from human parts.

Unlike Mary Shelley's original, the creature (portrayed by Michael Sarrazin) was not ugly when first animated. (1974 TV version).

Frankenstein's creation came to life under his hands. But the scientist was disgusted with the ugliness of the monster. He left him alone and went to bed. The monster awakened him and Frankenstein ran away in fear.

The monster crept away into the forest. He was lonely and frightened, and was chased by villagers. He began to live in a kind of cave near the hut of a blind old man and his two grown children. Weeks passed. The monster, looking for human kindness, did secret good deeds for the cottage people. One day, he even talked to the blind man and was overjoyed not to be rejected.

The creature is a social success at the opera in the 1974 TV version.

The creature begins to lose his handsome looks. But he still longs for acceptance and love. Above action is from the 1974 TV version.

But soon the old man's children returned. They drove away the hideous being. The monster was over come with anger and sadness. He burned down the cottage and vowed revenge on the human race that hated him so.

A small boy met the monster in the woods. Thinking to make the boy his friend, the monster grabbed him. "Let me go!" screamed the boy. "I will tell my papa, Monsieur Frankenstein! He will punish you!"

Hearing the name of his creator, the monster went wild. He strangled the boy who was William, the younger brother of Victor Frankenstein.

A servant girl was blamed for the murder and hanged. But the scientist knew that his monster was the real killer. He set out to put his creation to death with his own hands.

Instead, it was the monster who had revenge on Frankenstein. The creature murdered the scientist's dearest friend, Clerval. Then he strangled Frankenstein's bride, Elizabeth.

The fiendish laugh of the monster echoed through the Swiss Alps. Frankenstein set out to follow and destroy him.

The hunter and the monster he followed went northward. For months, Frankenstein followed the monster. They went into Russia, to the northernmost land in Europe.

The monster stole a dog sled and went northward onto the ice. Frankenstein followed . . . only to be picked up by the ship.

The scientist, worn out by his journey, sank into a coma that leads to death. Somehow, the monster knew this and came to the ship.

"Farewell, Frankenstein!" said the monster. "My spirit will sleep in peace." The creature leaped out of the cabin window into the blackness of the Arctic Ocean . . .

To his death? Of course not. Frankenstein's monster will live on and on as long as people like a good horror story.

Frankenstein's immortal monster.

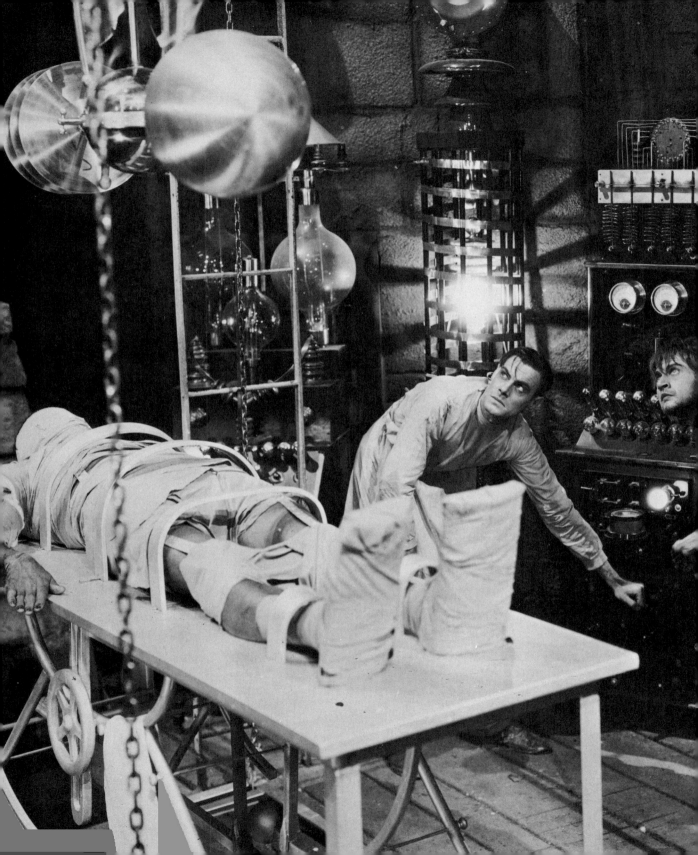

MAD SCIENTISTS

by Ian Thorne

Reprinted 1978

Library of Congress Catalog Card Number: 76-051149.

International Standard Book Numbers:
0-913940-70-4 Library Bound
0-913940-77-1 Paperback

Design - Doris Woods and Randal M. Heise.

MAD SCIENTISTS

FORBIDDEN KNOWLEDGE

The horror-movie scene is one we all know.

It is a laboratory. Tables are covered with strange glassware. Liquids bubble and steam. Odd electrical machines stand about. They may have blinking lights. Or if the movie is an old one, sparks may snap from them. There may be cages of animals. Or perhaps an operating table with — gasp! — a human subject strapped to it.

Then the man of science enters. He is ready for action. A strange gleam is in his eye.

Someone rushes in to plead with him. It may be a friend. It may be a wife or daughter. Or even a fellow scientist with more sense.

"Don't do it, Doctor! Don't perform the experiment! There are some things man was not meant to know!"

But the scientist only smiles. Fools may try to stop him, but he is not afraid! He will perform the experiment. He must know if his idea is correct!

The person who tried to stop the scientist turns away sadly. "No good will come of this, Doctor. You're mad! Mad, I tell you!"

Of course the scientist is mad. And of course his experiment will have a horrible ending. The search for "forbidden" knowledge will bring tragedy to others. It will bring doom to the scientist himself, too.

That is always the plot of "mad scientist" movies.

Fu Manchu and his lovely but evil daughter take good care of their death-ray machine. Boris Karloff and Myrna Loy starred in **The Mask of Fu Manchu** *(1932).*

Mr. Hyde.

The oldest of the movie mad scientists is Dr. Henry Jekyll. The poet Robert Louis Stevenson wrote The Strange Case of Dr. Jekyll and Mr. Hyde in 1886. Just one year later, it became a successful stage play. The first silent movie version came out in 1908. That was two years before Thomas Edison's movie, Frankenstein. (Another mad scientist story!)

Fredric March played both the good Dr. Jekyll (above) and the evil Mr. Hyde.

The best movie version of Jekyll and Hyde was made in 1931. It starred Fredric March, who won an Academy Award for it.

Dr. Jekyll and Mr. Hyde is the story of the two natures of the human soul. The good and the evil. Good Dr. Jekyll set free the evil person within himself. He was changed into a monster called Mr. Hyde.

9

It happened in London in the late 1800's. A brilliant young doctor, Henry Jekyll gave a speech. Hundreds of fellow scientists and students listened.

Jekyll said: "London is full of fog. It has cut through our brains and limited our sight. We are men of science. We should be curious and bold. We should look into the wonders of the human brain. We should look into the very soul of man!"

The audience murmured.

"I believe man has two selves. One is good. The other is evil. If we could separate the two, the good might become better. Then the so-called evil would fulfill itself and trouble us no more.

"In my experiments, I find that certain chemicals have the power . . ."

The speech ended. Dr. Jekyll bowed to applause. Next he hurried to his hospital to take care of a poor old woman. The trip made him late for a party that evening.

His loved one, Muriel Carew, was at the party with her father. Henry and Muriel hoped they would be able to marry soon. However, old General Carew wanted them to wait. He insisted on it.

Henry had to agree. Even so he was in a fury. After the party, he walked home with his friend, Lanyon. As they passed through a shabby street they heard screams.

Henry Jekyll speaks to his fiancee, Muriel Carew (Rose Hobart). Her father, General Carew (Halliwell Hobbes) and Jekyll's friend, Dr. Lanyon (Holmes Herbert) listen.

Jekyll and Lanyon hurried toward the noise. They found a pretty blonde woman struggling with a rough looking man. Jekyll moved in and hauled the man away.

The woman yelled "Hit me, will he? Blast his dirty mug! He's killed me! Broken me jaw!"

She was Ivy Pierson, a woman of the streets. She was also young and beautiful. Dr. Jekyll helped her up the stairs to her room.

Ivy said: "It's awful kind of you to look after me. Anyone can see that you're a real gent."

The doctor examined Ivy's injuries. They were not serious. "You'll be quite well in a few days."

Ivy looked at the doctor with grateful eyes . . . How different she was from cool Muriel! Different, but appealing, in spite of her rough manners.

Ivy reached out her arms. Dr. Jekyll could not help responding. They kissed.

At that moment, Lanyon came into the room!

Jekyll tried to make a joke of it. "I'll call that kiss my fee!" he said, then he and Lanyon left.

Jekyll's friend was icy. "I thought your behavior was shocking. Have you forgotten Muriel?"

"Of course not. It was simply an instinct —"

"You ought to control those instincts," said Lanyon.

"It can't be done. Unless . . . we separate the two natures within us. If my theory is correct, it can be done."

Lanyon only laughed. "You're mad," he said.

Henry Jekyll went on with his experiments. He searched for the chemical that would let him separate the good and the evil in human nature. He worked without sleep, without food.

His servant brought him a note. It was from Muriel. She scolded him for not coming to a dinner party he had promised to attend. How foolish!

He felt he was near success in his experiment. The chemical would surely work! He would try it on himself. Tonight. He wrote a note to Muriel. It said:

"If I die, it is in the cause of science. I shall love you always, through eternity."

Then he drank the chemical.

Henry Jekyll stood before a mirror. He saw himself begin to change . . .

Pain wracked his body. His face twisted. His mild, kindly expression vanished. His nose became ape-like. His teeth jutted, like those of an ape: His forehead became low. His eyes were deep sunk. They were shining with wickedness.

"Free!" he cried. "And they called me mad! Ah! If they could see me now!"

The evil side of Henry Jekyll had taken over his body. All of the evil in his human nature was now free.

Henry Jekyll drinks the chemical then watches his appearance and mood change from good to evil.

He put on his cloak and hat. He bounded outside into the rain. Free! Free to do all the evil he wished to do! No one could stop him!

He went looking for Ivy Pierson. She was at work — singing in a music hall. He went to that place and took a table. Ivy was singing:

"Champagne Ivy is me name. Good for any game at night, me boys."

She was invited to sit at the table with the man in the cloak. "My name is Hyde," he said. "I have admired you."

At first, Ivy (Miriam Hopkins) is fascinated by Mr. Hyde.

Ivy was cool with Mr. Hyde. She drank champagne with him. She noticed his expensive clothes. He was ugly but he had money. And Ivy was poor.

"I want you," Mr. Hyde told Ivy. "And what I want, I get."

Ivy could not resist Mr. Hyde. He promised her nice clothes and jewels. He told her he loved her. He said he would give her a nice place to stay. She would live like a real lady.

Ivy believed him. When she found out the evil truth about Mr. Hyde, it was too late.

He was a human monster. He beat her. He was evil to her in a thousand ways — as a cat tortures a mouse that it plans to kill.

Ivy wanted to escape from Mr. Hyde, but she was too frightened. For a whole month, he kept her in his power.

And then he went away!

Mild Dr. Henry Jekyll appeared once more. The chemical had changed him back into his normal self. Back in his lab, he wrote a note to Ivy. He enclosed a large sum of money and had his servant deliver the note to her.

Henry visited Muriel. "I have been ill," he told her. "It was a sickness of the soul. I've played with dangerous knowledge. I've walked a strange and terrible road. Help me find my way back!"

Ivy begs Dr. Jekyll to save her from the evil Hyde.

Muriel promised she would help him. They would be married at once. Her love would heal him.

That evening, Henry Jekyll was full of joy. But then he had a visitor. It was Ivy Pierson.

"I've come to thank you for the money," she said. "But I can't keep it. Hyde wouldn't allow it. He's a beast! Oh, help me, sir. You're good and kind. Help me get away from him."

Jekyll realized at last what he had done. As "Mr. Hyde," he had done dreadful things to this poor woman. He decided to give up his experiments forever.

"You will never see Hyde again," he promised.

Ivy left, reassured. Jekyll went ahead with the plans for his marriage. He drank no more of the chemical. All that was behind him.

But was it? His evil self had been freed: Would it stay chained, deep within his soul? One evening, Jekyll sat on a park bench. He saw a cat creep up on a bird and kill it. It awakened a memory within him . . .

To his horror, Jekyll felt himself begin to change! Mr. Hyde had refused to die. He was returning. He was taking over Henry Jekyll's body.

"It is death! Death!" cried Mr. Hyde.

He went to look for Ivy.

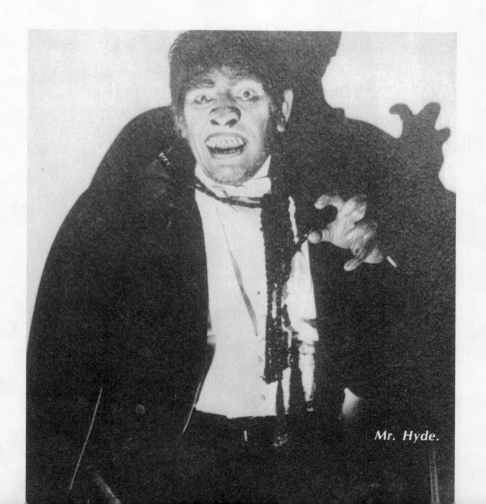

Mr. Hyde.

She was alone in her room celebrating. She had believed Dr. Jekyll when he said that Hyde would trouble her no more.

But suddenly, he was there!

"You thought I wouldn't come back!" he snarled. "You believed that hypocrite, Jekyll. You went down on your knees to him, the man I hate! You wanted him to love you!"

"No, no, it ain't so!" screamed Ivy.

I'll give you a lover now," said Hyde. "His name is Death!"

Ivy tried to run away. But Hyde was after her with superhuman speed. He seized her. His hairy hands closed about her throat.

There came a pounding at the door. Ivy's screams had brought other people to see what was wrong. Hyde crashed through them and ran off into the fog.

A policeman came and looked at poor Ivy's body. "A monster did this," he said.

"I know him!" said the landlady. "His name is Hyde!"

Hyde knew he was in great danger. He had to change back into Dr. Jekyll. He sent a note to his friend Lanyon. It asked Lanyon to get the chemicals from Jekyll's lab.

Lanyon did so. Then Hyde came to his house and asked for the chemical. Lanyon would not give it to him. He thought Hyde had kidnapped Jekyll.

"I will show you," Hyde said. He drank the chemicals before Lanyon could stop him.

"You sneered at the wonders of science," said Mr. Hyde. "Now look! Look!"

Lanyon saw the monstrous Hyde change into Dr. Jekyll. "I am a murderer," the doctor confessed. "Help me, Lanyon. Help me!"

But his friend said: "There is no help for you."

Jekyll returned to his home. He prayed. "Oh, God, forgive me. I've done something no man should do."

He went to Muriel Carew. He told her he could not marry her. Then he left. As he went, he began to change and became Mr. Hyde!

Jekyll tells Muriel that he cannot marry her.

Hyde came into the music room where Muriel sat weeping. He crept up on her.

Muriel looked up and screamed in horror. Her father, General Carew, heard her. He rushed into the room. He and Hyde began to fight. They went crashing through the French doors and onto the patio.

Hyde raised his cane. It had a heavy metal knob. He struck General Carew again and again. Then he ran away, just as the police came up.

Later, Lanyon looked sadly at General Carew's body. "I know whose cane that is," he told the police. "I can take you to the man."

They set off for Jekyll's laboratory.

Hyde attacks General Carew.

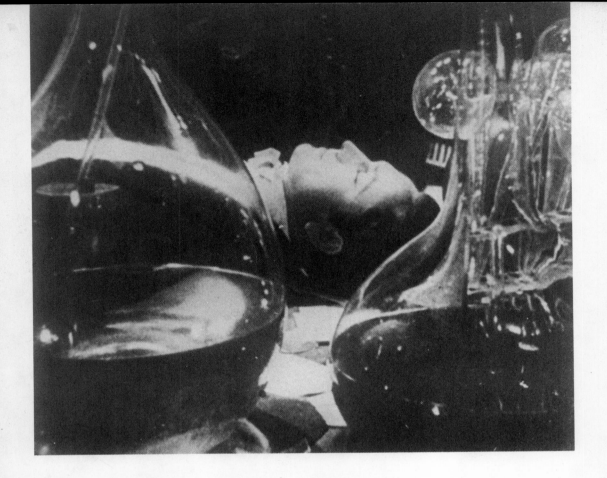

Lanyon and the police confronted Dr. Jekyll.

"Hyde is not here," the doctor said. "He went out the back way."

Lanyon said: "He has not gone away. There is your man!" And he pointed at Dr. Jekyll.

At that moment, Jekyll began to change. He became Hyde right before their eyes. He grabbed a knife.

A police inspector drew his gun and fired.

Mr. Hyde fell dying. As his life slipped away, he began to change once more. The good and the evil of Henry Jekyll merged into a single man. And then he died.

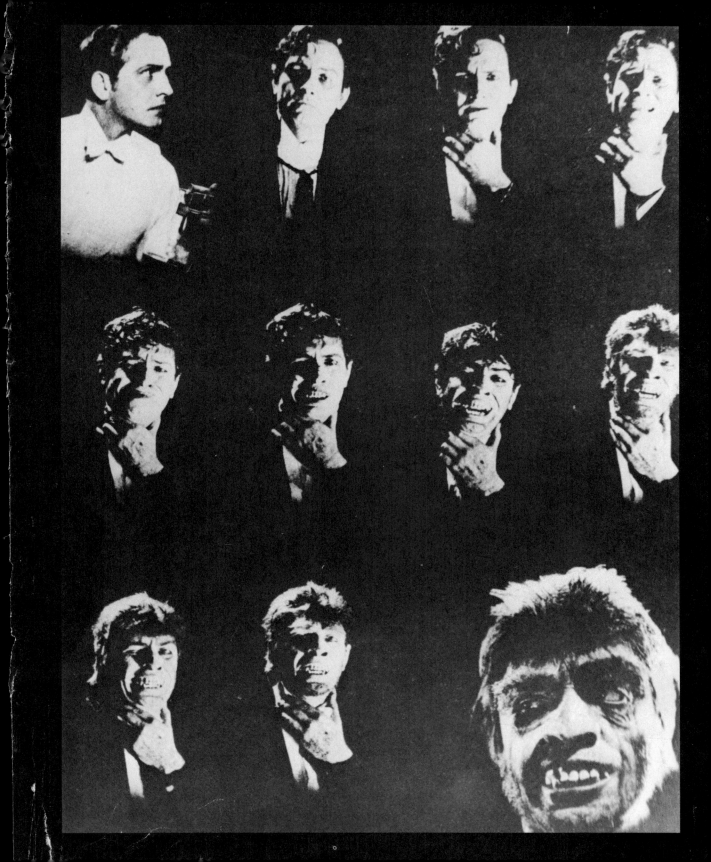

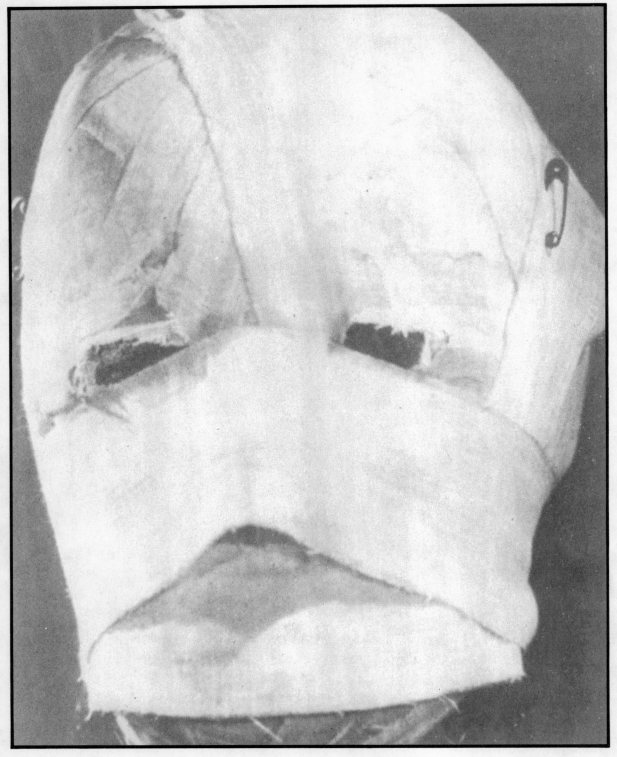

THE INVISIBLE MAN

Another of the greatest mad scientist movies was The Invisible Man. It was made in 1933, based on novel written by H. G. Wells in 1897.

The story began on a snowy day in England . . .

A man came to the village Inn at Iping. His face was heavily bandaged. Dark goggles covered his eyes.

"I want a room and a fire," he told the innkeeper. Then, as the inn's customers stared, he went upstairs and made himself at home.

During the next few days, boxes arrived for the stranger. He kept to himself. He worked alone in his room, which he turned into a chemical laboratory.

Meanwhile, the innkeeper and the villagers began to worry. Who was this man? What was he up to?

"I think he must be a criminal!" one man said.

"Call in the constable!" said a woman.

The village policeman was called. He and a small group of villagers went to the stranger's room. They forced their way in.

The bandaged man was angry. "So you want to know who I am! I'll show you!"

He took off the dark goggles. There's a little souvenir for you." Then removed a false nose. "And another for you!"

"He's all eaten away!" exclaimed the horrified policeman.

The stranger ripped off false hair. Next he began to unwind the bandages that covered his head.

Suspicious villagers confront the mysterious stranger.

But there was no head.

"It's easy, if you're clever!" said the stranger. The villagers stared as if turned to stone. The headless man took off coat, shirt, tie, pants, and underwear. There was no body underneath!

"Just a few chemicals, mixed together," said the voice of the stranger. "That's all it takes."

"Blimey — he's invisible!" cried a villager.

"Just a few chemicals," laughed the stranger. "A little of this and that. Injected under the skin. Flesh and bone just fade away! An invisible man can rule the world. Nobody will see him come. Nobody will see him go. He can hear every secret. He can rob the rich . . . and kill."

And a terrible laugh rang out in the room. The Invisible Man was free and he was mad.

The Invisible Man ignores the pleadings of Gloria Stuart, who plays Flora Cranley.

Housekeeper Una O'Connor knows there's something fishy about this fellow.

That same evening, the Invisible Man went to the home of his friend, Dr. Kemp.

"It is I, Jack Griffin!" said the voice of the unseen one. "For five years I worked on my discovery. Monocaine! It has made me invisible. And it has lit up my brain!"

Griffin told his friend he planned to rule the world. "We'll begin with a reign of terror. A few murders —"

Kemp was frightened. The monocaine had not only made Griffin invisible, it had driven him completely insane.

The police inspector feels an invisible body!

Griffin killed a policeman. His fiancee, Flora Granley, tried to reason with him. He brushed her aside. "I shall offer my secret to the world. I will sell it for millions! The winning country can sweep the earth with invisible armies!"

Griffin began his reign of terror. He killed and robbed. The police tried without luck to capture him.

Then one night, the Invisible Man was cornered in a barn. People set fire to it. When Griffin ran out, his footprints were seen in the snow.

A policeman fired his pistol. There in the snow was the outline of an invisible body . . .

The Invisible Man was taken to a hospital. Crying, Flora leaned over the bed where he lay. A doctor told her it was impossible to treat invisible wounds. Griffin was dying.

"I wanted to do something great," Griffin whispered. "I was so poor. I had nothing to offer you, Flora."

His voice grew weaker and weaker. "My darling, I have failed. I got involved in things that man must leave alone."

With that, the Invisible Man died. As Flora and the movie audience watched, he slowly became visible. Jack Griffin, portrayed by actor Claude Rains, was visible only in death.

The insane Dr. Moreau (Charles Laughton) is attacked by his pitiful monsters.

MORE MAD SCIENTISTS

The mad scientist movies of the 1930's were a great success. Then, as now, many people did not understand science too well. It was almost like magic. Scientists had powers that common folks only dreamed of. And if a scientist went mad — why, there was no telling what he might do!

Another novel by H. G. Wells became a horror classic, The Island of Lost Souls. The mad doctor of this film was played by Charles Laughton.

Dr. Moreau tried to speed up evolution. He experimented with animals on his island. The results were "manimals" — half-human beings with different, horrible animal bodies.

Dr. Moreau used the manimals as his slaves. His greatest experiment produced a panther-woman named Lota. A shipwrecked sailor named Parker came to the island. Dr. Moreau decided he would be Lota's mate.

Then a rescue expedition arrived, looking for Parker. Dr. Moreau ordered his manimals to kill the captain of the expedition.

Once they had tasted blood, the manimals revolted from Dr. Moreau's cruel rule over them. In an awful climax, the half-human creatures dragged Dr. Moreau away. They planned to "experiment" on him just as he had tortured them in the name of science.

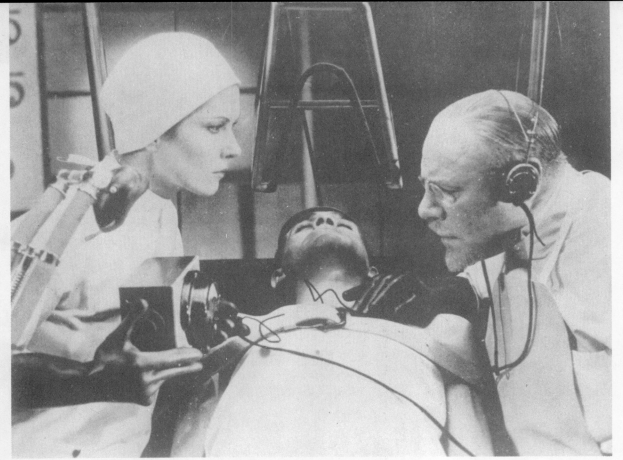

Marguerite Churchill and Edmund Gwenn make a big mistake in reviving Boris Karloff in The Living Dead.

Dr. Moreau was an evil man. But some of the mad scientists were not bad. They just misused their knowledge. In The Walking Dead (1936), Edmund Gwenn played a doctor. He experimented with ways to bring dead people back to life.

When John Ellerman, played by Boris Karloff, was framed for murder and executed, Gwenn brought him back to life. The experiment was not a complete success since Karloff was turned into a revenge seeking zombie. He destroyed each of the evil doers who had framed him. He then died, once again his savage work being done.

The brilliant Karloff played a mad scientist himself in many films. He was an evil Oriental in The Mask of Fu Manchu (1932). He was stopped from his attempt to master the world with a death-ray.

In The Invisible Ray (1936), he tampered with secrets of the universe and became radioactive. An interesting beginning to the movie stated: "The scientific dream of today may well become the scientific fact of tomorrow."

In The Man They Could Not Hang (1939), Karloff was executed when his mechanical heart caused death instead of life. However, the scientist was restored to life by his own invention. He punished those who had destroyed him.

Karloff in a scene from **The Man They Could Not Hang.**

Many mad scientist movies used the idea of bringing the dead back to life.

One of the best of these was Revenge of the Zombies. This classic of horror was filmed in 1944. The mad scientist was played by John Carradine, who also played mad doctors in Captive Wild Woman, Invisible Man's Revenge, and Return of the Ape-Man.

As a mad zombie-maker, Carradine created many walking dead folk to do his bidding. Then his lovely wife died after an unsuccessful operation. Carradine could not stop from bringing her back to semi-life — as a zombie.

Of course, the evil doctor gets what's coming to him in the end. The zombies gang up on the fellow who has upset their sleep. And one more mad scientist bites the dust in Hollywood.

John Carradine made a career out of horror movies. He became one of the well known screen villains and still was active in the 1970's. His sons joined him in show business, carrying on their father's work.

John Carradine is about to get what's coming to him in Revenge of the Zombies.

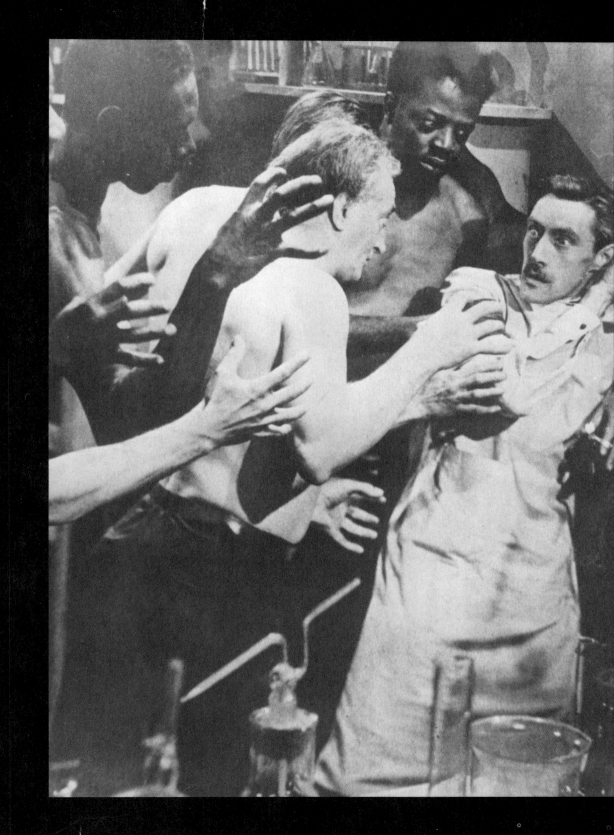

A different kind of mad scientist appeared in Dr. Cyclops (1939). This was the first horror film to be made in color. It starred Albert Dekker as the insane Dr. Thorkel.

Thorkel lived deep in the jungle. He invented a ray-machine that could shrink living things to one-sixth their normal size. A group of scientists came to visit Thorkel. He decided to use them in his experiments. They were given an instant reducing treatment under the ray.

Five tiny people, less than a foot tall, escaped from Thorkel's lab. They decided they would have to kill the doctor before he killed them.

The midgets fled from dangers such as a giant cat and huge chicken. Dr. Thorkel himself hunted them with a butterfly net.

Finally, they tried to make the scientist powerless by breaking his glasses. They smashed one lens, then Thorkel discovered them. In anger, he killed one of the mini-people. He chased the others outside. They led him toward an open well.

Blind in one eye, the mad scientist tripped in. He clung to a rope. The bravest of the tiny men went down the rope and forced Thorkel to let go. And so the mad scientist was gone forever.

Ten days later, the effects of the ray wore off. The mini-people returned to normal size.

Albert Dekker seeks out tiny victims in **Dr. Cyclops.**

The mad scientist in Tarantula (1955) didn't make things small. Instead, he made them large!

Leo G. Carroll played Dr. Deemer, who didn't start out mad. Deemer experimented with glands. He wanted to treat diseases caused by glands that did not work the way they should.

Deemer's experiments worked on animals. He made both a rat and a guinea pig grow large. But then the doctor's assistant tried the serum. It turned him into a monster.

It also drove him insane.

Leo. G. Carroll checks a giant rat and guinea pig.

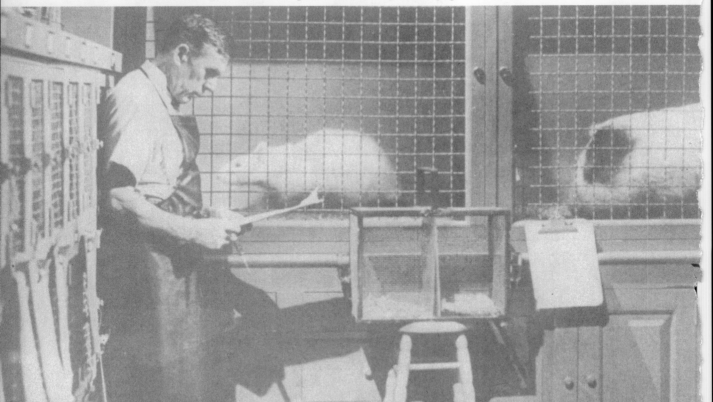

Giant Tarantula.

The crazed assistant injected the doctor with his own medicine. Presto! Another evil human! The two of them fought. A cage holding one of Deemer's experimental animals was broken. The beast escaped.

It was a tarantula — ten feet across!

Still growing, the spider terrorized Arizona. In the movie's climax, it was hunted down and killed.

Many other "giant critter" movies have been made. They are among the most popular horror films. There have been giant ants, giant grasshoppers, giant mantises, giant chimps and even giant rabbits.

Those mad scientists just never learn to leave well-enough alone!

Among the best of the "giant critter" movies was The Fly (1958).

A French Canadian scientist built a machine that would teleport living things. That is, it would dissolve a thing to its atomic particles, transmit the particles across space, then put them back together again.

The scientist tried to teleport himself across the room. He got into the booth of the machine. He dissolved, but he did not know that there was a fly in the booth with him!

When the scientist was put back together again, he had the head and claw of the fly. The tiny insect had a human head and hand.

The scientist tried very hard to catch the fly. If he had it, he might be able to correct the mistake. But the insect stayed out of reach.

In a moving ending, the fly-headed man writes a note on a blackboard to his wife: "I love you." He asks her to destroy the results of his experiment.

They go to a factory owned by their family. The scientist places his fly-head and claw under a huge press. His wife presses the button that crushes the evidence of the scientific mistake.

And the fly with the human head? It is eaten by a spider!

Vincent Price is attacked by the fly-headed monster.

The maddest of the mad scientists was Victor Frankenstein. When people think of mad doctors, they remember Frankenstein's lab. The machine. The lightning flash. The monster coming to life.

Frankenstein's monster became a killer. He turned on his own master. Too late, Victor realized that he had tried to "play God." In this movie, as in other mad scientist stories, there is the idea that certain kinds of knowledge are forbidden.

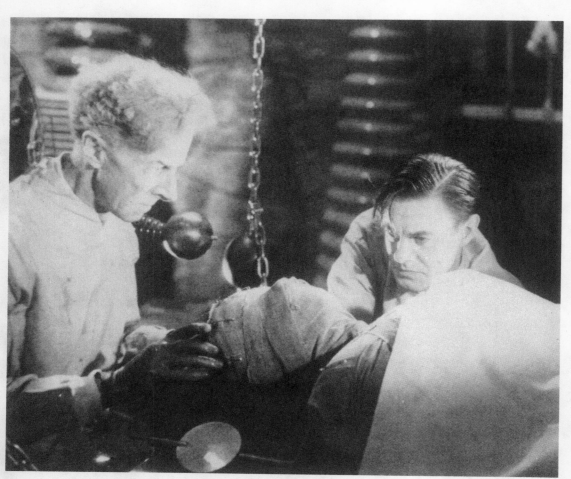

Both Ernest Thesiger and Colin Clive play mad scientists in **Bride of Frankenstein** *(1935).*

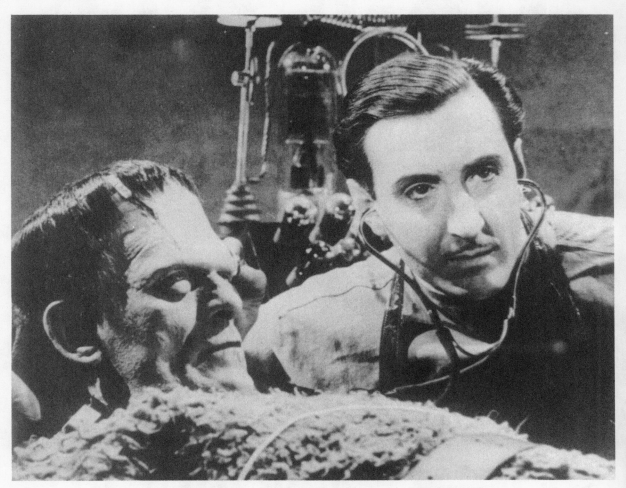

Boris Karloff shows signs of life under the care of Basil Rathbone in
Son of Frankenstein (1939).

Today, people go to mad scientist movies and en-
joy a good scare. Some of the older horror films, such
as the Fu Manchu stories, are even funny.

But there is a serious question we may ask after
the movies are over. Are there limits to science? Are
there some things it is better not to tamper with? People asked that question after the atomic bombs were
made. They are asking it today, when science is on the
edge of being able to create life.

MONSTERS

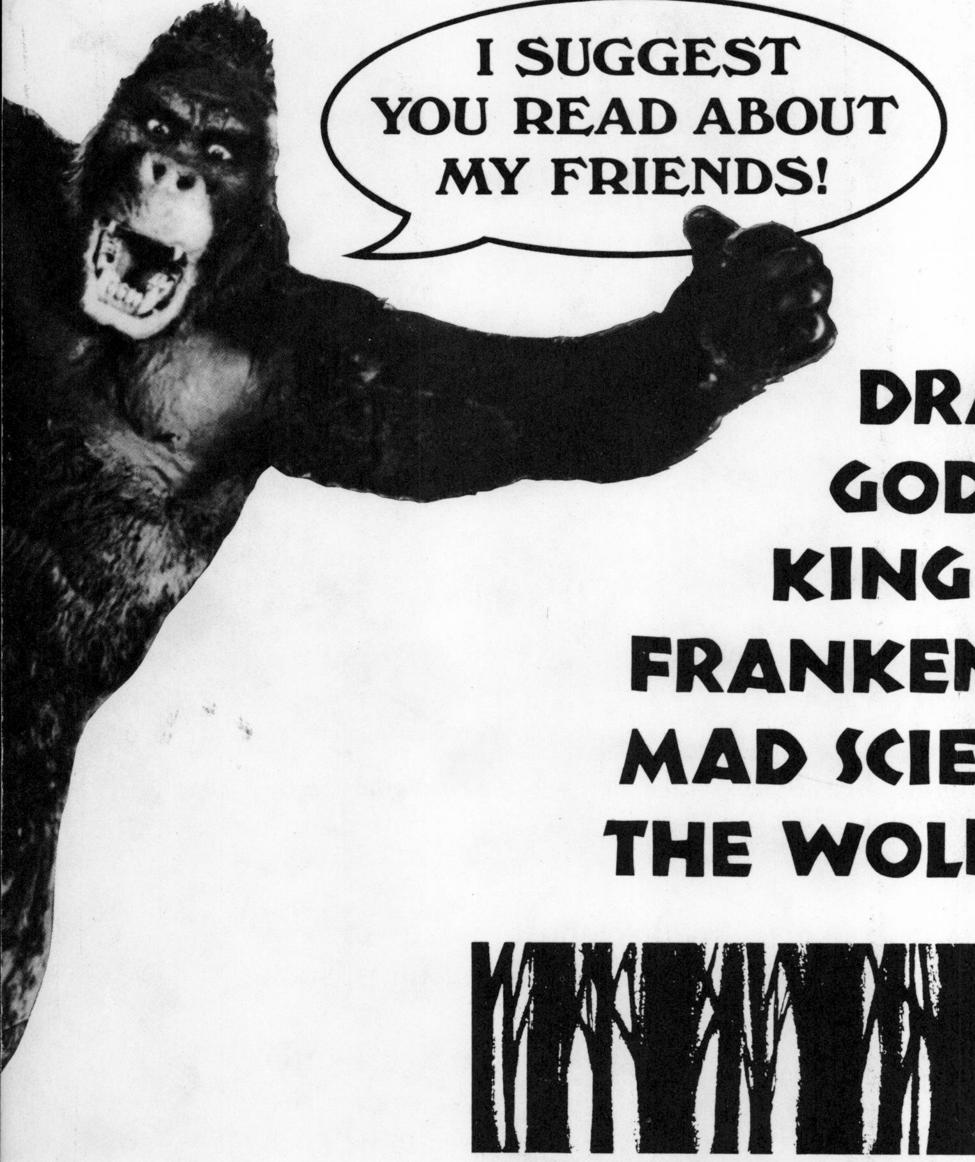